GW00361009

IT'S PARTY TIME!

To: ....

From: ....

Date: ....

Time: ....

Place: ....

....

RSVP: ....

Email/Phone: ....

IT'S PARTY TIME!

To: ....

From: ....

Date: ....

Time: ....

Place: ....

....

RSVP: ....

Email/Phone: ....

IT'S PARTY TIME!

To: ....

From: ....

Date: ....

Time: ....

Place: ....

....

RSVP: ....

Email/Phone: ....

IT'S PARTY TIME!

To: ....

From: ....

Date: ....

Time: ....

Place: ....

....

RSVP: ....

Email/Phone: ....

IT'S PARTY TIME!

To: ....

From: ....

Date: ....

Time: ....

Place: ....

....

RSVP: ....

Email/Phone: ....

IT'S PARTY TIME!

To: ....

From: ....

Date: ....

Time: ....

Place: ....

....

RSVP: ....

Email/Phone: ....

IT'S PARTY TIME!

To: ....

From: ....

Date: ....

Time: ....

Place: ....

....

RSVP: ....

Email/Phone: ....

IT'S PARTY TIME!

To: ....

From: ....

Date: ....

Time: ....

Place: ....

....

RSVP: ....

Email/Phone: ....

IT'S PARTY TIME!

To: ....

From: ....

Date: ....

Time: ....

Place: ....

....

RSVP: ....

Email/Phone: ....

THANK YOU SO VERY MUCH...

THANK YOU SO VERY MUCH...

THANK YOU SO VERY MUCH...

THANK YOU SO VERY MUCH...

THANK YOU SO VERY MUCH...

THANK YOU SO VERY MUCH...

THANK YOU SO VERY MUCH...

FANTASTIC WORK!

Presented to

....

For

....

....

Date ....

FANTASTIC WORK!

Presented to

For

Date

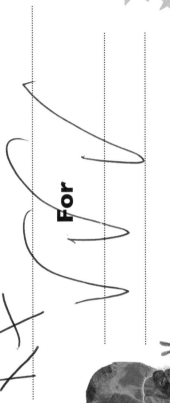

FANTASTIC WORK!

Presented to

....

For ....

....

Date ....

FANTASTIC WORK!

Presented to

....

For

....

....

Date ....

FANTASTIC WORK!

Presented to

For

Date

FANTASTIC WORK!

Presented to

....

For

....

....

Date ....

FANTASTIC WORK!

Presented to

....

For

....

....

Date ....

FANTASTIC WORK!

Presented to

....

For

....

....

Date ....

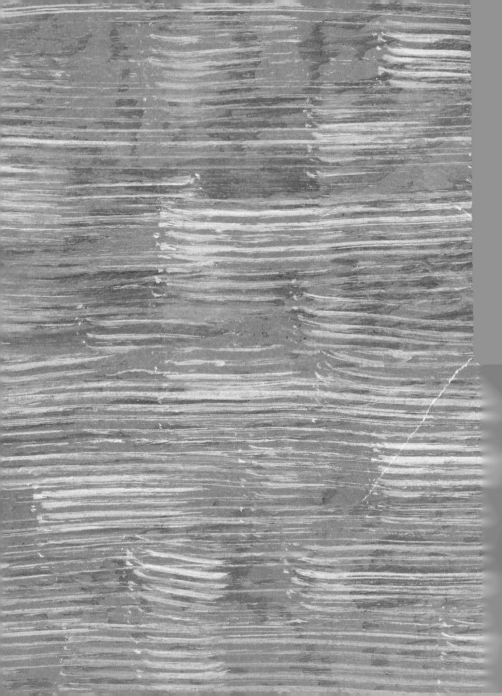

GOOD BEHAVIOUR AWARD

Presented to

Because

Date

GOOD BEHAVIOUR AWARD

Presented to

....

Because

....

....

Date ....

GOOD BEHAVIOUR AWARD

Presented to

Because

Date ....

GOOD BEHAVIOUR AWARD

Presented to

....

Because

....

....

Date ....

GOOD BEHAVIOUR AWARD

Presented to

....

Because

....

....

Date ....

GOOD BEHAVIOUR AWARD

Presented to

....

Because

....

....

Date ....

GOOD BEHAVIOUR AWARD

Presented to

Because

Date

GOOD BEHAVIOUR AWARD

Presented to

Because

Date

GET WELL SOON...

Sorry to hear you're feeling poorly!

GET WELL SOON...

Sorry to hear you're feeling poorly!

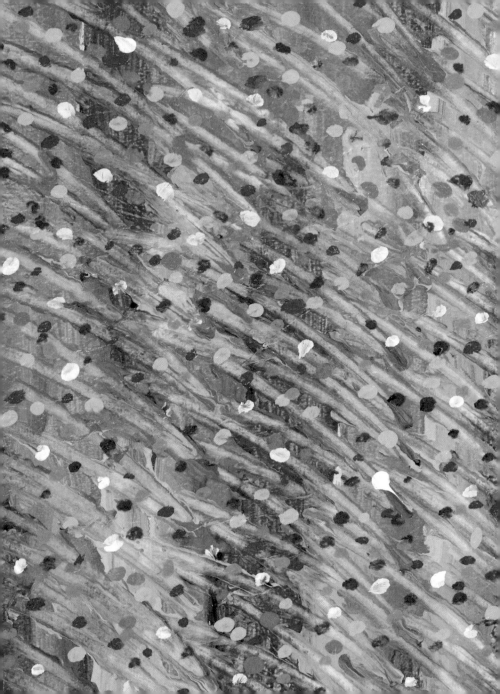

GET WELL SOON...

Sorry to hear you're feeling poorly!

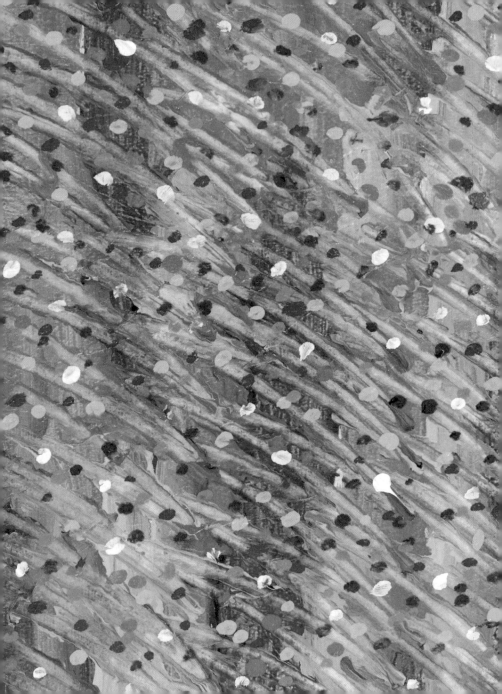

GET WELL SOON...

Sorry to hear you're feeling poorly!

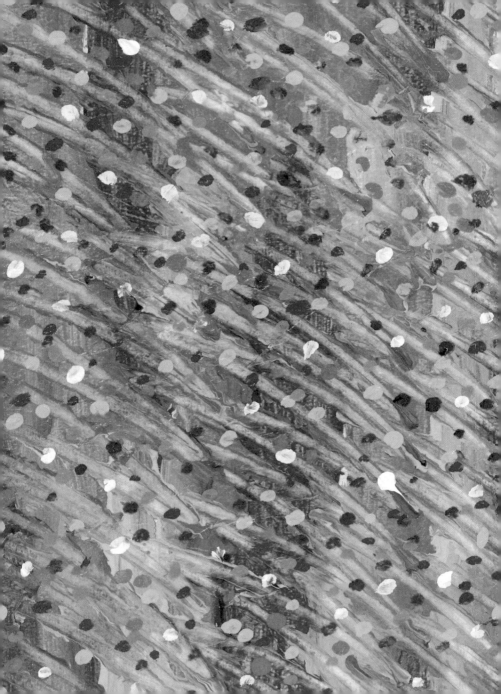

GET WELL SOON...

Sorry to hear you're feeling poorly!

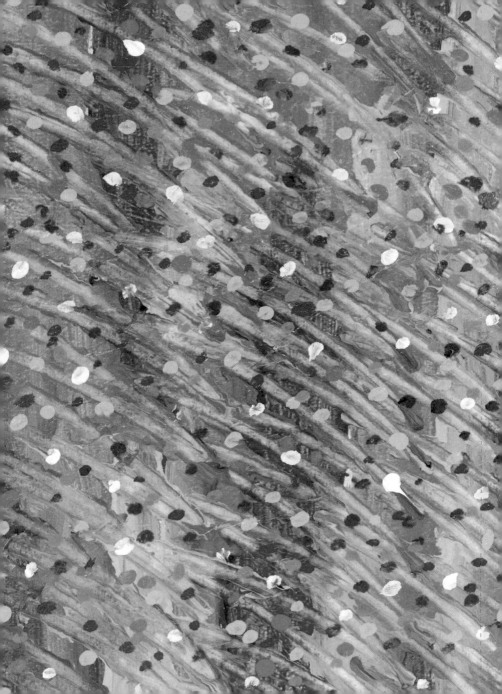

GET WELL SOON...

Sorry to hear you're feeling poorly!

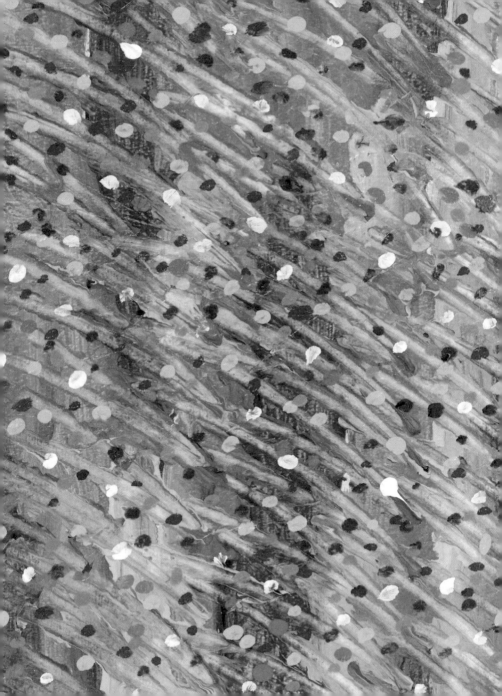

GET WELL SOON...

Sorry to hear you're feeling poorly!

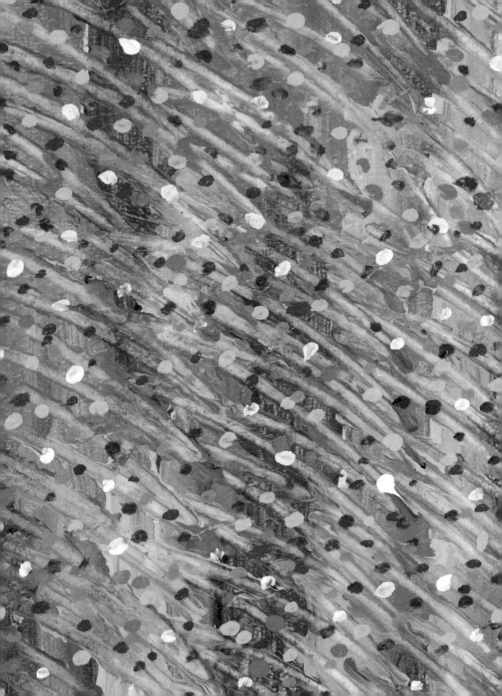

GET WELL SOON...

Sorry to hear you're feeling poorly!

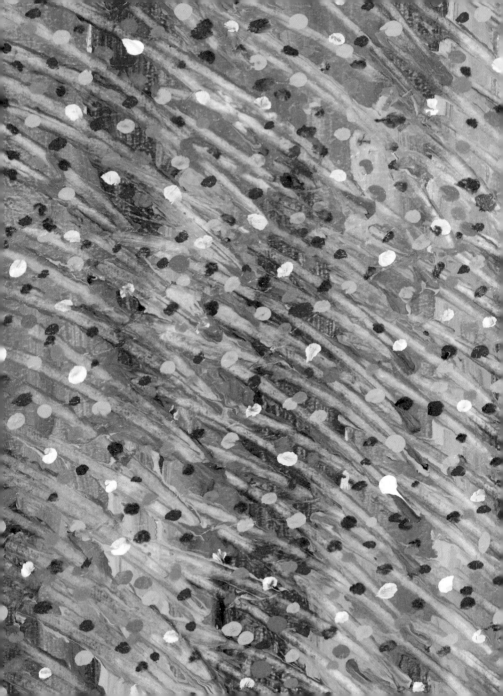

GET WELL SOON...

Sorry to hear you're feeling poorly!

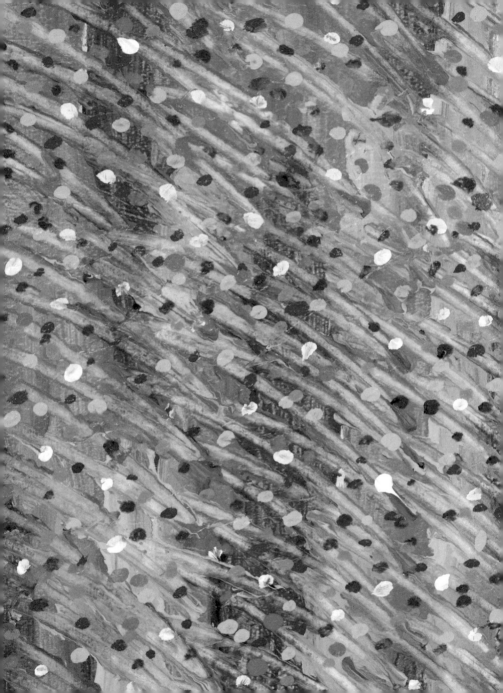

JUST TO SAY...

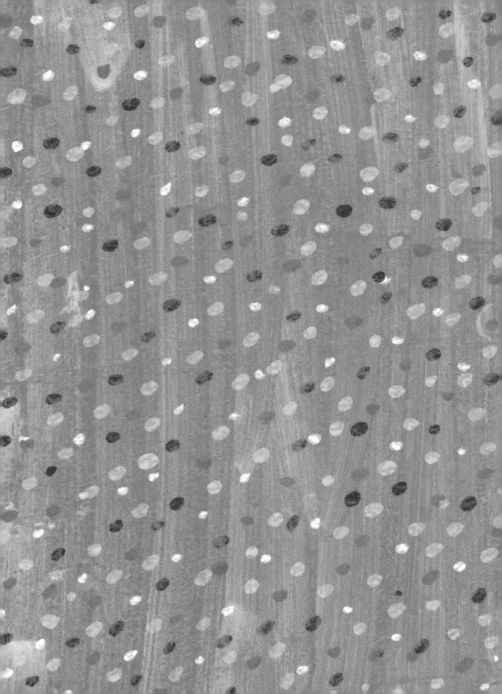

JUST TO SAY...

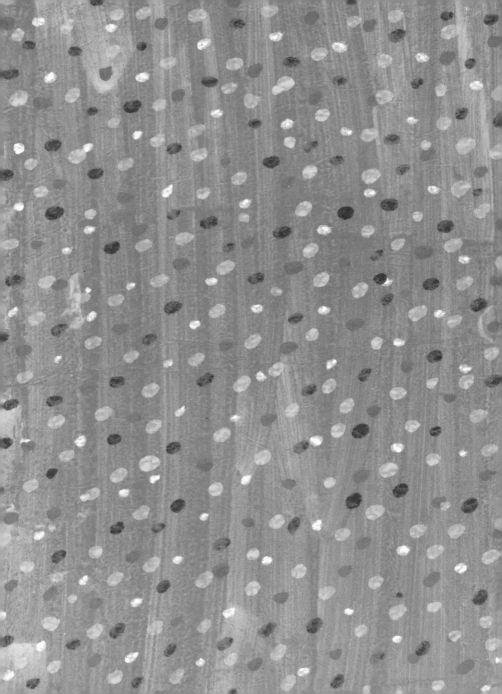

JUST TO SAY...

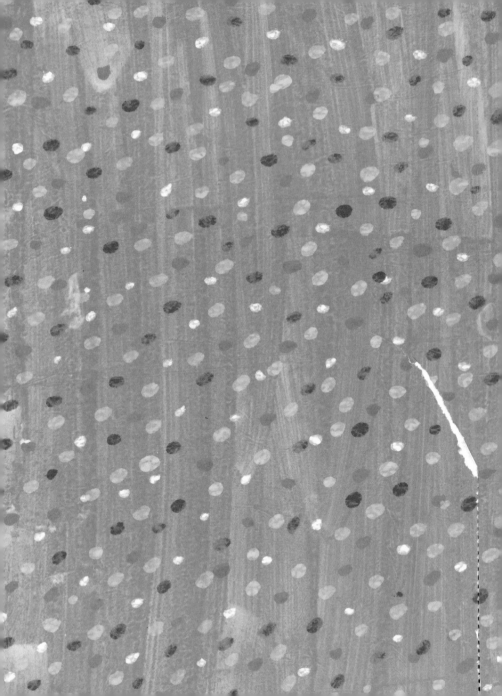

JUST TO SAY...

JUST TO SAY

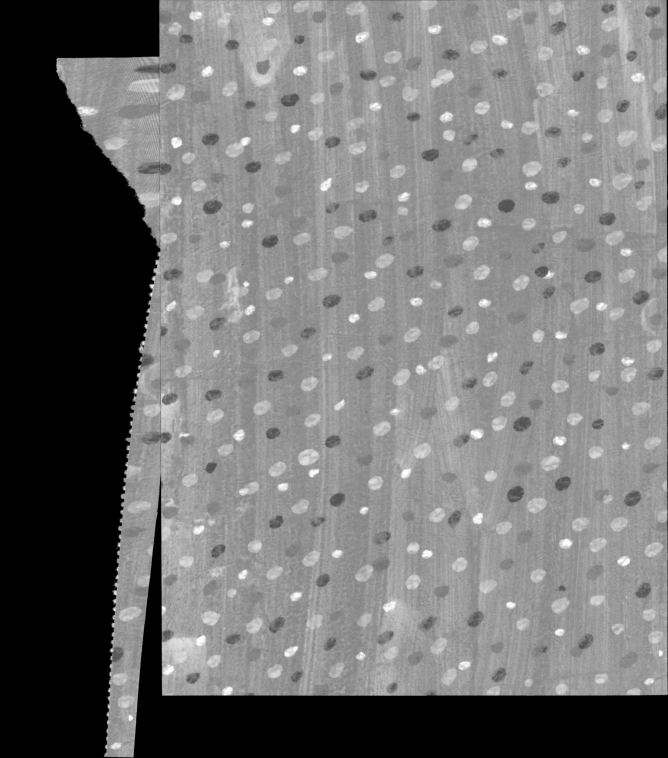

JUST TO SAY...

JUST TO SAY...

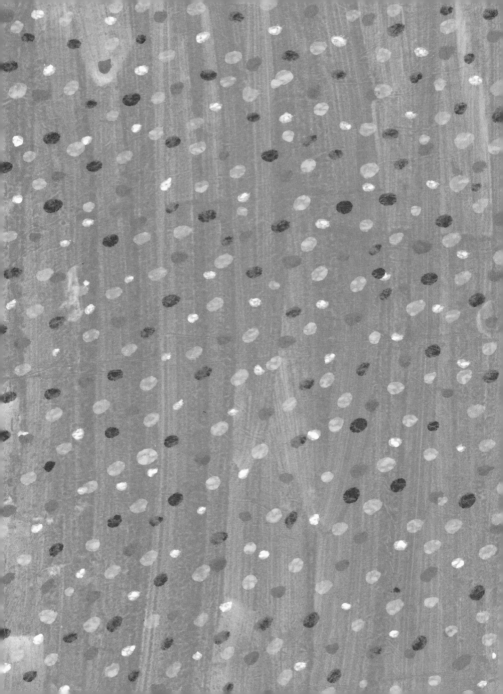

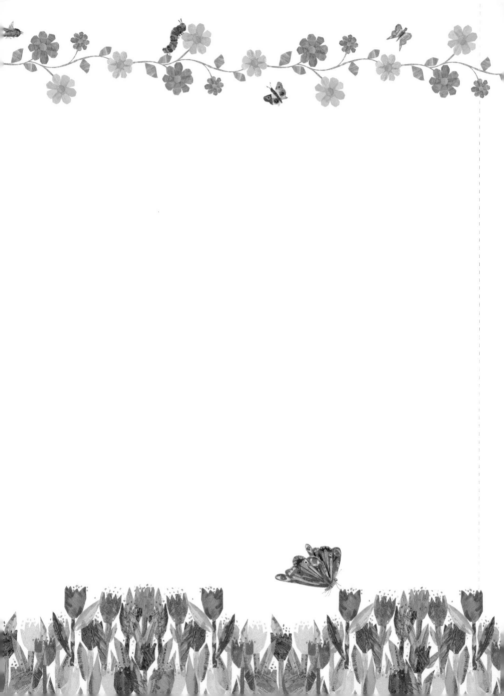

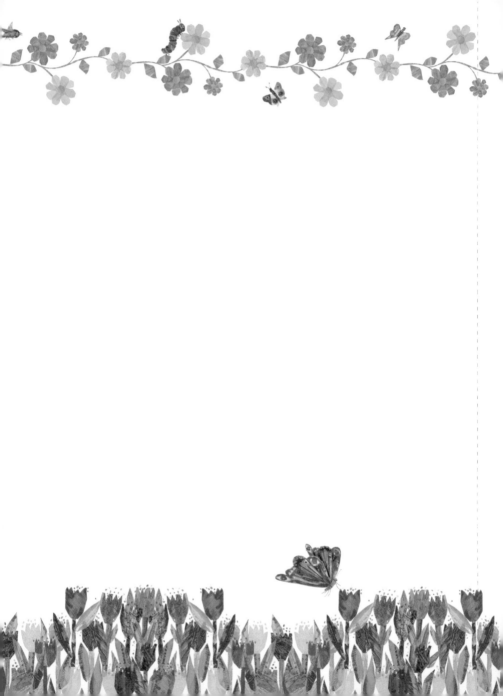

L